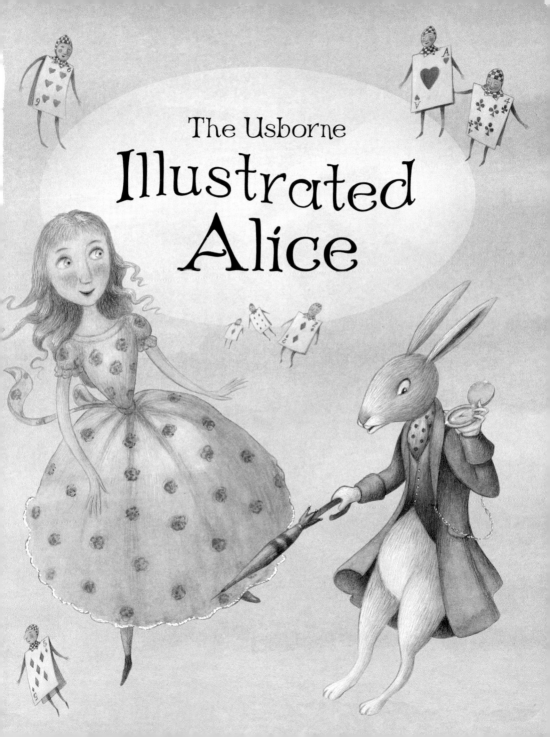

The Usborne
Illustrated
Alice

The Usborne
Illustrated
Alice

Based on the stories by Lewis Carroll
Adapted by Lesley Sims
Illustrated by Mauro Evangelista
Designed by Louise Flutter

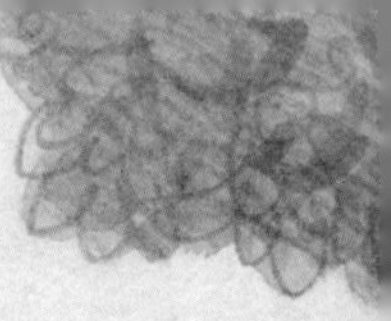

Contents

Alice's Adventures in Wonderland

Contents

Chapter 1

Down the rabbit hole

Alice was getting tired of sitting with her sister. She had tried reading her sister's book, but it didn't have any pictures or conversation. "And what is the use of a book," thought Alice, "without pictures or conversation?"

She was just wondering whether to pick some daisies for a daisy-chain when a White Rabbit ran past. Now, seeing a rabbit isn't so very remarkable.

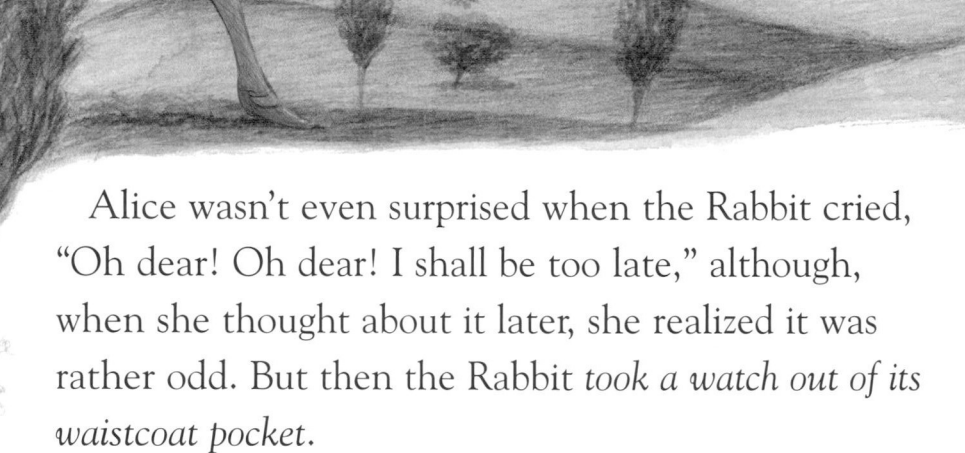

Alice wasn't even surprised when the Rabbit cried, "Oh dear! Oh dear! I shall be too late," although, when she thought about it later, she realized it was rather odd. But then the Rabbit *took a watch out of its waistcoat pocket*.

10

Alice jumped to her feet at once, for it flashed across her mind that she had never seen a Rabbit with either a waistcoat pocket or a watch to take out of it.

Burning with curiosity, she ran across the field after him and was just in time to see him pop down a large rabbit-hole.

Alice followed, never once thinking how she was to get out again.

At first, the hole went on like a tunnel. Then it dipped and Alice was falling down a deep well. Either the well was very deep or Alice fell slowly, for she had plenty of time to look around. The walls were full of shelves and cupboards, with pictures hung here and there.

Down, down, down. Would the fall never end? "I must be near the middle of the earth," said Alice. And then, "I wonder if I shall fall right through?"

Down, down, down. There was nothing else to do so Alice carried on talking to herself. "Dinah will miss me very much." (Dinah was her cat.) "I hope they remember your milk, Dinah. I wish you were here." She was daydreaming about walking hand in hand with Dinah when *thump* she landed on a heap of dry leaves and the fall was over.

Oh my ears and whiskers,
how late it's getting!

Not in the least hurt, Alice
jumped up and looked around. A
long passage was ahead of her and
the White Rabbit was hurrying
down it. Alice ran like the
wind, but the Rabbit
turned a corner...
and vanished.

Alice was in a hall with doors down both sides – but they were all locked. She walked down one side and up the other, wondering how she would ever get out. Suddenly she saw a glass table with a tiny golden key on it. It was too small for most of the doors – or the doors were too big for the key – but at last she found a tiny locked door hidden behind a curtain.

The key fit perfectly! And beyond the door was the most beautiful garden Alice had ever seen.

"Oh if only I could shrink," thought Alice. She had begun to think that in this place anything might be possible. But she couldn't shrink, so she went back to the table, hoping to find another key to a bigger door.

This time she found a bottle with a label saying *Drink me*. "That wasn't here before," Alice said, checking it carefully. Since it wasn't marked *Poison*, she took a sip. It tasted so delicious (a mix of cherry-tart, custard, toffee and hot buttered toast), that she very soon finished it off.

"What a curious feeling!" Alice said next. "I think I'm shrinking!" She smiled – now she could explore the lovely garden.

But alas for Alice, she had forgotten the key and the tiny door had shut. The key was on the glass table and its legs were far too slippery to climb. After three tries, Alice fell to the floor and began to cry. "This won't help," she told herself sharply. She wiped her eyes and saw a glass box lying under the table. The box held a small cake.

"I'll eat it," said Alice. "If I grow I can reach the key. If I shrink I can creep under the door. Either way, I'll get into the garden."

Chapter 2

The pool of tears

"Curiouser and curiouser!" cried Alice,
who had shot up at an alarming rate.
"Goodbye feet!"

She only stopped growing when her head
hit the ceiling. Quickly, she grabbed
the key and hurried to the door. But
getting through the tiny
door now was more
hopeless than ever.

Alice sat down and began to cry again, sobbing and
sobbing until a vast pool of tears spread around her.
After a while, she heard pattering feet and dried
her eyes. It was the White Rabbit, trotting along in a
great hurry, and carrying
a pair of gloves and a fan.

Alice felt so desperate that she was ready to ask for
help from anyone. When the Rabbit came near, she
began in a low, timid voice, "If you please sir..."

19

The Rabbit jumped in the air, dropped the gloves and the fan, and scurried away as fast as he could. Alice picked them up, and, as the hall was very hot, started to fan herself.

"Dear, dear! How very strange everything is today," she said.

Alice was wondering if she had turned into someone else when she noticed she was shrinking again. She soon realized it was the fault of the fan she was holding and dropped it before she shrank away altogether.

20

"That WAS a narrow escape," said Alice, a little frightened but very relieved she was still there. "And now for the garden." But the door was shut again and somehow the key was back on the table. "Now things are worse than ever," said Alice. "This is too bad."

As she said these words, her foot slipped and *splash* she fell into a pool of salty water. Her first thought was that she had somehow fallen into the sea. Then she remembered the tears she had cried when she was so tall.

She was just wishing she hadn't cried so much when she heard a splashing. She thought it was a walrus or hippopotamus, until she remembered how small she was and saw it was only a mouse, who had fallen in too.

The pool was soon crowded with the birds and animals who had fallen in, including a Duck, a Dodo, a Lory and an Eaglet. Alice led the way and the whole party swam to the shore.

22

Chapter 3

A caucus race

It was a very odd party that gathered on the bank, and all of them were dripping wet, cross and uncomfortable. The first question, of course, was how to get dry.

"The driest thing I know is History," said the Mouse and began to recite some facts.

"The best thing to get us dry," said a Dodo firmly, "would be a Caucus-race."

"What IS a Caucus-race?" asked Alice.

"Why," said the Dodo, "the best way to explain it is to do it."

There was no 'One, two, three, go!' Everyone began and stopped when they liked, so it was not easy to know when the race was over.

After about half an hour, when they were quite dry, the Dodo suddenly called out, "The race is over and everybody has won!"

He pointed to Alice. "She will give prizes."

In despair, Alice put her hand in her pocket and pulled out a tin of peppermints. There were exactly enough for one each.

"But she must have a prize too," said the Mouse.

"Of course," said the Dodo. "What else do you have in your pocket?"

Alice took out a thimble. The Dodo solemnly presented it to her and everyone cheered.

Alice thought the whole thing was absurd but they all looked so serious, she didn't dare laugh. Instead she bowed and accepted her thimble.

The next thing was to eat the peppermints. This caused some noise and confusion as the large birds complained they couldn't taste theirs and the small ones choked and had to be patted on the back. But it was over at last and they sat in a circle and begged the Mouse to tell them a story.

"Mine is a long and sad tale," said the Mouse, with a sigh.

"It IS a long tail certainly," said Alice, looking down at the Mouse's tail, "but why do you call it sad?" And she kept on puzzling about it while the Mouse was speaking.

"You're not listening," the Mouse said crossly, getting up and walking away.

"Please come back and finish your story," Alice called after it, but the Mouse only shook its head and walked a little faster.

"I wish I had our Dinah here," Alice said aloud, to no one in particular. "She'd soon fetch it back!"

"And who is Dinah?" asked one of the birds.

"Dinah's our cat," Alice replied eagerly.

This comment caused a sensation, with all the creatures running off. Alice was left alone feeling sad, until she heard the pattering of footsteps.

Chapter 4

The White Rabbit's house

It was the White Rabbit, trotting back again and looking about anxiously. "Mary Ann!" snapped the Rabbit as he noticed Alice. "Run home and fetch me some gloves and a fan."

Alice was too frightened to say anything and ran
off in the direction he pointed. "He thinks I'm his
maid!" she thought. "But I'd better take him his
gloves and fan."

As she said this, she came upon a small
house with *W. Rabbit* on a brass plate
outside.

She went in without knocking and ran upstairs in case she met the real Mary Ann and was thrown out before she had the fan and gloves.

"How strange it is," thought Alice, "to be running errands for a rabbit. I expect Dinah will be ordering me around next!"

By this time, she had found her way into a little room with a table, and on it lay a fan and several pairs of tiny white gloves. She took up the fan and a pair of gloves, and was just going to leave, when her eyes fell upon a little bottle.

There was no label this time with the words *Drink me*, but nevertheless she uncorked it and put it to her lips. "*Something* interesting is sure to happen," she said to herself. "I do hope I'll grow large again, for really I'm quite tired of being such a tiny little thing!"

And grow she did. Before she had drunk half, her head was pressing against the ceiling. She went on growing... until one arm was out of the window and her foot was stuck up the chimney.

"Mary Ann!" called the Rabbit crossly. "Where are my gloves?"

Alice trembled, quite forgetting that she was now a thousand times larger than the Rabbit and had no reason to be scared.

When the Rabbit couldn't open the door – because Alice's elbow was against it – he went around to the window.

Alice waved her
hand and heard a shriek.

"Pat! Where are you?"
the Rabbit shouted and
Alice heard a new
voice reply.

"Over here sir."

"Well, tell me," said the Rabbit, "what's
in this window?"

"An arm, sir," said the voice.

"An arm, you goose!" said the
Rabbit. "Whoever saw one that
size? Take it away!"

33

"And send the lizard down the chimney," the Rabbit added.

As soon as Alice heard a little animal scrabbling inside the chimney, she gave a sharp kick and the lizard came shooting out.

"There goes Bill," said a voice.

"A barrowful will do," the Rabbit said next.

"A barrowful of what?" thought Alice.

She didn't have long to wonder, for the next moment a shower of little pebbles came rattling in at the window. To Alice's surprise, the pebbles turned into tiny cakes as they lay on the floor. "If I eat one of these cakes," she thought, "it's sure to make SOME change in my size. And as I can't possibly grow any larger, I expect I'll grow smaller."

Alice shrank at once. As soon as she could squeeze through the door, she fled, and she didn't stop running until she reached a forest.

"The first thing I have to do," she decided when she had caught her breath, "is to grow to my right size. Then I must find a way into that lovely garden."

It was an excellent plan. The only problem was how to do it. "I suppose I should eat or drink something," she thought. "But what?"

Alice looked around and saw a mushroom. She peered over the edge to see a large caterpillar, quietly minding its own business.

Chapter 5

The Caterpillar's advice

The Caterpillar and Alice looked at each other for a while.

"Who are *you?*" the Caterpillar asked finally, in a sleepy voice.

"I, I hardly know, sir," said Alice.

"What do you mean?" demanded the Caterpillar. "Explain yourself!"

"I can't explain *myself*," said Alice, "because I'm not myself. I keep changing size, I can't remember things and it's all very confusing."

"Try reciting a poem," said the Caterpillar.

Clearing her throat, Alice began.

"You are old, father William,"
the young man said,
"And your hair has become very white;
And yet you incessantly stand on your head ~
Do you think, at your age, it is right?"
"In my youth," father William replied to his son,
"I feared it might injure the brain;
But now that I'm perfectly sure I have none
Why, I do it again and again."

40

"That's not right," said the Caterpillar.

"Not QUITE right, I'm afraid," said Alice, "some of the words have changed."

"It is wrong from beginning to end," said the Caterpillar decidedly, and there was silence for some minutes.

The Caterpillar was the first to speak. "What size do you want to be?" it asked.

"Oh, I'm not particular as to size," Alice hastily replied. "Only one doesn't like changing so often, you know."

"I DON'T know," said the Caterpillar.

Alice said nothing.

"Are you content now?" said the Caterpillar.

"Well, I should like to be a LITTLE larger, sir, if you wouldn't mind," said Alice, "three inches is such a wretched height to be."

"It is a very good height indeed!" said the Caterpillar angrily, rearing itself upright as it spoke. (The Caterpillar was exactly three inches high.)

The Caterpillar was silent again. Then it yawned and slid down off the mushroom. "One side will make you grow taller, the other will make you grow smaller," it remarked.

"One side of what?" asked Alice.
"The mushroom," said the Caterpillar.

"Now which is which?" wondered Alice when she had broken off two pieces of mushroom.

She nibbled one piece and felt a blow as her chin struck her foot. Somehow, though she could barely open her mouth, she managed to nibble on the other piece. This time, she shot up so far she lost sight of her shoulders. Finally, by nibbling one piece at a time, she reached her right size.

She walked on through the forest until she came to a little house. "I don't want to scare anyone," she said, and ate some more mushroom to shrink herself.

Chapter 6

Pig and pepper

As Alice looked at the house, a fish dressed as a footman ran up and rapped wetly on the door. It was opened by a frog. Alice crept closer.

For the Duchess.
An invitation from
the Queen.

From the Queen.
An invitation for the
Duchess.

When the fish had gone, Alice went to the door and knocked.

"There's no use knocking," said the Frog. "I'm on the same side as you. Besides, they're making too much noise to hear."

So Alice marched straight in and found herself in a large kitchen. A grumpy Duchess sat in the middle holding a baby, and a cook was leaning over the fire stirring a large cauldron.

"There's too much pepper in that!" Alice said to herself and started to sneeze.

There was certainly a lot of pepper in the air. Even the Duchess sneezed occasionally and, as for the baby, it was sneezing and howling alternately without a moment's pause. The only things in the kitchen that did not sneeze were the Cook and a cat, which was grinning from ear to ear.

"Please would you tell me," said Alice, a little timidly, "why your cat grins like that?"

"It's a Cheshire cat," said the Duchess, "and that's why."

"I didn't know that Cheshire cats grinned," remarked Alice. "I didn't know cats could grin."

"They all can," said the Duchess, "and most of 'em do."

"I don't know of any that do," Alice said, very politely.

"You don't know much," said the Duchess, "and that's a fact."

47

Alice didn't like this comment at all but before she could change the subject, the Cook began throwing pans, plates and dishes at the Duchess and the baby. "Oh please watch what you're doing," cried Alice. "If everybody minded their own business," the Duchess said in a hoarse growl, "the world would go around a deal faster than it does." With that, she began to sing a sort of lullaby, while tossing the baby up and down.

Speak roughly to your little boy
And beat him when he sneezes:
He only does it to annoy
Because he knows it teases.

"Here," she finished suddenly, flinging the baby at Alice. "You look after it, if you like. I must get ready to play croquet with the Queen."

Alice caught the baby and left before they were hit by a flying frying-pan. The baby grunted and Alice glanced down. To her surprise, it had turned into a pig, so she decided to put it down. It made a rather handsome pig, Alice thought.

49

She watched it run off and looked up to see the Cheshire Cat grinning at her.

"Cheshire Cat," she began, shyly, "where should I go now?"

"Well THAT way," the Cat said, waving its right paw, "lives a Hatter and THAT way," waving the other paw, "lives a March Hare. Visit either you like, they're both mad."

"But I don't want to visit mad people," Alice remarked.

"Oh, we're all mad here," said the Cat and, slowly, it started to vanish.

Chapter 7

A mad tea party

"As it's May, the March Hare might not be quite so mad," Alice thought and decided to visit him.

The March Hare was sitting at a large table in front of his house, having tea with the Hatter. A Dormouse sat between them, fast asleep.

"No room! No room!" they cried when they saw Alice.

"There's PLENTY of room!" said Alice indignantly, sitting down.

"Your hair wants cutting," said the Hatter.

"You shouldn't make personal remarks," Alice said. "It's very rude."

The Hatter opened his eyes very wide on hearing this, but all he said was, "Why is a raven like a writing-desk?"

Then he took out his watch and shook it. "Two days wrong," he complained. "I told you butter wouldn't suit the works!" he added, looking angrily at the March Hare.

"It was the BEST butter," the March Hare meekly replied.

"Yes, but some crumbs must have slipped in as well," the Hatter grumbled. "You shouldn't have put it in with the bread-knife. Have you guessed the riddle yet?" he asked, turning to Alice.

"I give up," she replied. "What's the answer?"

"I haven't the slightest idea," said the Hatter.

Alice sighed. "You shouldn't waste time asking riddles with no answer," she said.

"Oh Time and I aren't speaking," said the Hatter. "We argued at a concert given by the Queen of Hearts. I sang a song, you know."

Twinkle, twinkle little bat!
How I wonder what you're at!
Up above the world you fly
Like a tea-tray in the sky.
Twinkle, twinkle little bat!
How I wonder what you're at!

"I'd hardly finished the first verse, when the Queen shouted that I was murdering Time. It's been tea-time ever since."

"This is the stupidest tea party I was ever at in all my life," thought Alice and walked off. No one took the least notice of her going and when she looked back, they were trying to put the Dormouse into the teapot.

Back in the forest, Alice noticed a tree with a door in the trunk. Curious, she stepped inside.

Once more she found herself in the long hall. She took the key from the glass table, unlocked the door and then nibbled some mushroom until she was smaller. At last, she could enter the beautiful garden.

Chapter 8

Meeting the Queen

A large rose-tree stood near the entrance of the garden. The roses growing on it were white, but three gardeners were busily painting them red. Alice thought this very curious, and she went closer to watch.

57

Alice's Adventures in Wonderland

"Would you tell me," said Alice, a little timidly, "why you are painting those roses?"

"Well Miss," began one of the gardeners in a low voice, "this here ought to have been a RED rose-tree, and–"

"The Queen! The Queen!" another one cried and all three threw themselves flat on their faces.

"And who arc *these*?" said the Queen, staring at them.

"How should *I* know?" said Alice.

"Off with her head!" screamed the Queen.

"Nonsense!" said Alice.

The Queen glared at the rose tree and turned back to the gardeners. "Off with *their* heads." Quickly, Alice threw them into a pot to hide them.

"Time for croquet," roared the Queen.

Alice had never played such a curious game – the balls were hedgehogs and the mallets were flamingoes.

Everyone played at once and the Queen stomped among the players, shouting, "Off with their heads!"

Alice began to feel uneasy. She was looking around for some way of escape, when she noticed a curious sight in the air. After watching it for a minute or two, she made it out to be a grin.

"How are you getting along?" said the Cat, as soon as there was enough mouth for it to speak.

Alice waited for its ears before replying. "They don't follow any rules," she complained. "And as for the Queen..."

Just then she saw the Queen listening in.

"...she's too good," Alice finished quickly.

The Queen smiled.

"Who *are* you talking to?" asked the King, going up to Alice.

"A friend of mine, a Cheshire Cat," said Alice.

"I don't like the look of it," said the King.

"Off with his head!" said the Queen.

Instantly, the Cat's body vanished.

"I can't cut off a head if there's no body to cut it from," declared the executioner.

"Anything with a head can be beheaded," argued the King.

"Everyone will lose their heads in a minute," said the Queen, and sent for the Duchess to get her cat.

The croquet game went on until the Queen's soldiers had arrested almost everyone. While the King was letting them all go again, a voice suddenly shouted out, "Time for the trial!"

Chapter 9

Who stole the tarts?

Alice followed everyone into a crowded court. "Herald, read the accusation!" said the King. The White Rabbit blew three blasts on his trumpet, unrolled a parchment scroll, and read aloud:

The Queen of Hearts
She made some tarts
All on a summer day.
The Knave of Hearts
He stole those tarts
And took them
quite away!

"Consider your verdict!" the King said to the jury.

"Not yet, not yet!" the Rabbit interrupted. "There's a great deal to come before that."

"Call the first witness," said the King.

The White Rabbit blew three blasts on the trumpet and called out, "First witness!"

The first witness was the Hatter, who came in holding a teacup and a slice of bread and butter.

"I beg pardon, your Majesty," he began nervously, "for bringing these in, but I hadn't quite finished my tea when I was sent for."

"You ought to have finished," said the King. "Take off your hat."

"It isn't mine," said the Hatter.

"Stolen!" the King exclaimed, turning to the jury, who instantly wrote it down.

"I keep them to sell," the Hatter explained. "I've none of my own."

Here the Queen put on her spectacles, and began staring at the Hatter, who turned pale.

"Give your evidence," said the King, "and don't be nervous, or I'll have you executed on the spot."

The Hatter was now so scared, he shook.

"You may go," said the King and the Hatter hurriedly left the court room.

Alice had begun to feel an odd sensation. She was growing larger.

"Call the next witness!" said the King and in walked the Duchess's cook.

"Give your evidence!" said the King.

"Shan't," said the Cook.

"Call the next witness," the King said again.

Alice was curious to see who it was for they had heard no evidence at all yet. Imagine her surprise when the White Rabbit read out, at the top of his shrill little voice, the name 'Alice!'

Chapter 10

Alice's evidence

"Here!" Alice cried, jumping up. But she'd grown so big, she sent the jury box flying and everyone fell out.

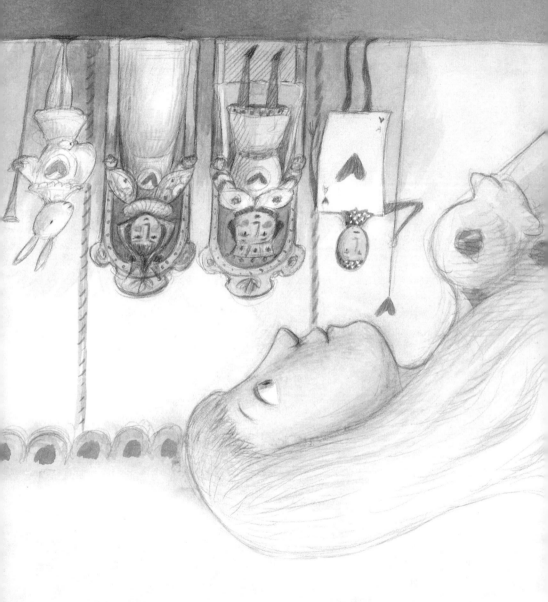

They lay sprawling about, reminding her of a bowl of goldfish she had accidentally upset the week before.

"Oh, I BEG your pardon!" she exclaimed in dismay, and began picking them up again as quickly as she could. The accident with the goldfish kept running through her head, and she had a vague sort of idea that they must be collected at once and put back into the jury-box, or they would die.

"What do you know about this business?" the King asked Alice.

"Nothing," said Alice.

"Let the jury consider their verdict," the King announced.

"Sentence first, verdict later," said the Queen.

"Stuff and nonsense!" said Alice.

"Hold your tongue!" snapped the Queen.

"I won't!" said Alice.

"Off with her head!" the Queen shouted.

"Who cares about you?" Alice retorted.

Alice had grown to her full size by this time. "You're nothing but a pack of cards!" she went on, dismissively.

At this, the whole pack rose up into the air and came flying down upon her. She gave a little scream, half of fright and half of anger, and tried to beat them off...

...and woke up to find
herself back with her
sister, who was still
deep in her book.

"Was I asleep?" thought Alice. "Well, I've had a wonderful dream!" And she called for her sister to stop reading, so that she could tell her – as well as she remembered them – all these strange adventures of hers that you have just been reading about.

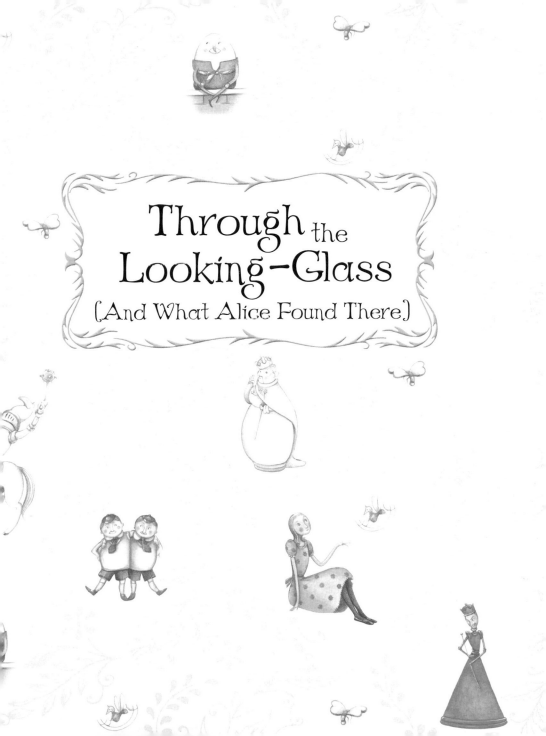

Through the
Looking-Glass

(And What Alice Found There)

Contents

This story is set in an imaginary world that is like a chessboard. So, lots of the characters you'll meet are pieces used in the game of chess: a Red King and Queen, a White King and Queen, Red and White Knights and Pawns.

Chapter 1

The looking-glass house

"Kitty," said Alice one day, "you look like the Red Queen. Can you play chess?" Kitty yawned.

"Don't be rude, Kitty," said Alice and held her up to the mirror. "Can you see through there?" she asked. "That's the looking-glass house and it's where you'll go if you don't behave. The room you can see through the glass is just the same as our drawing room, only the things go the other way around. Imagine what it's like to live there..." she went on.

"Let's pretend there's a way of getting into it somehow," Alice said next. "Let's pretend the glass has gone soft, so we can get through." She was up on the mantelpiece as she said this, though she hardly knew how she had done it.

"Oh!" she said then, for the glass was beginning to melt away in a bright silvery mist.

In another moment Alice was through the glass. She sat on the mantelpiece and stared. A chessboard lay on the floor and the pieces were strolling around. She could see Kings, Queens, Knights and Pawns, but none of them seemed to see her.

Alice spotted a book and jumped down to look at it. At first, she thought it was in a language she didn't know. Then she remembered she was in the looking-glass house and held it up to the glass. Now she could read it... though it still didn't make much sense.

JABBERWOCKY

'Twas brillig, and the slithy toves
Did gyre and gimble in the wabe;
All mimsy were the borogoves,
And the mome raths outgrabe.

"Beware the Jabberwock, my son!
The jaws that bite, the claws that catch!
Beware the Jubjub bird, and shun
The frumious Bandersnatch!"

He took his vorpal sword in hand:
Long time the manxome foe he sought
So rested he by the Tumtum tree,
And stood awhile in thought.

"Oh!" Alice cried suddenly. "If I don't hurry, I shall have to go back before I've explored anywhere."

She ran from the room and raced down some stairs, almost floating through the hall to the front door.

Chapter 2

A garden of talking flowers

Out in the garden, Alice saw a hill with a path that seemed to lead straight to it. "I'll see the garden much better from up there," she said.

But the path had more twists and turns than a corkscrew. Whichever way Alice went, she always ended back at the house.

"Oh it's too bad!" she cried. "I never saw such a house for getting in the way."

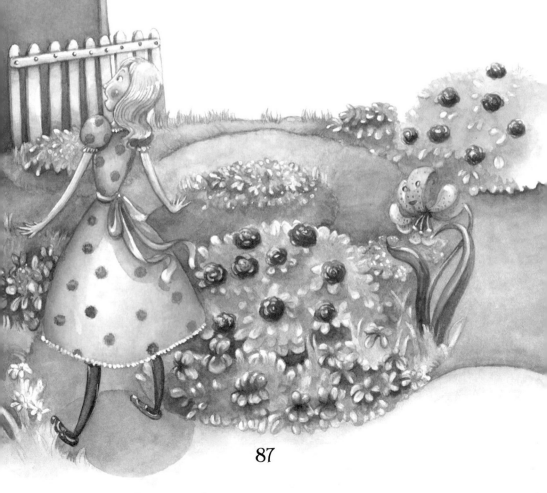

She turned to a flower waving gracefully
in the wind. "Oh Tiger-lily, I
wish you could talk."

"We can," said the Tiger-lily, "when
there's anyone worth talking to."

Alice was so astonished that, for a minute, she
couldn't speak herself. "Can all flowers talk?" asked
Alice after a while. "I've never heard any."

"Feel the ground," ordered the Tiger-lily.

"It's very hard," said Alice.

"In most gardens," the Tiger-lily said, "the beds are too soft. All the flowers are asleep."

"I never thought of that," said Alice. "Are there any people in this garden, besides me?"

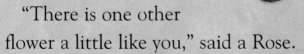

"There is one other flower a little like you," said a Rose.

Alice smiled. Perhaps there was another girl to play with.

"She's coming!" said a Marigold.

Alice looked around eagerly. But it was the Red Queen – and she seemed to have grown. When Alice had last seen her, she was only the size of a thumb. Now, she looked taller than Alice.

"I think I'll go and meet her," said Alice.

"You can't possibly do that," said the Rose. "I advise you to walk the other way."

This sounded like nonsense to Alice, so she said nothing but set off after the Red Queen at once. To her surprise, she soon lost sight of her.

After looking everywhere for the Queen, she finally spied her a long way off, and decided that this time she would try the plan of walking in the opposite direction.

It succeeded beautifully. She had not been walking a minute before she found herself face to face with the Red Queen and on the hill at last.

"Where are you going?" asked the Queen.

"I'm not sure," Alice replied. "I keep losing my way."

"Your way?" said the Queen. "All the ways around here belong to me. But why are you here at all?"

"I wanted to see the garden, your Majesty," said Alice. The Red Queen patted her on the head – which Alice didn't like at all – and led her up the hill.

From the top you could see all over the country, and what a strange country it was. A number of tiny little brooks ran straight across it from side to side, and the ground between was divided up into squares by little green hedges that reached from brook to brook.

"It's just like a chessboard!" said Alice.

"There ought to be some men moving around somewhere..." Alice peered into the distance. "And so there are," she added, in delight. "It's a great huge game of chess that's being played – all over the world – if it is a world. Oh what fun it is. How I wish I was one of them. I wouldn't even mind being a Pawn if I could join in."

She looked at the Red Queen shyly. "Though of course I should like to be a Queen best."

The Red Queen smiled. "That's easily managed. You can be the White Queen's Pawn if you like. You're almost in the Second Square already. When you get to the Eighth Square, you'll be a Queen."

Just at that moment, somehow or other, they began to run. All Alice knew was that they were running hand in hand and the Queen kept calling, "Faster! Faster!"

The most curious part was that, however fast they went, they never seemed to get anywhere.

"We haven't moved!" Alice panted when they finally stopped to rest.

"Of course not," said the Queen. "Here, it takes all the running you can do, to stay in the same place. To go somewhere else, you must run twice as fast."

You must be thirsty. Would you like a dry biscuit?

"Now, directions," said the Queen. "A Pawn – that's you – goes two squares in its first move. So you'll go very quickly through the Third Square, by railway I should think. In the Fourth Square you'll meet Tweedledum and Tweedledee – they're brothers you know."

"The Fifth Square has a shop and the Sixth belongs to Humpty Dumpty. The Seventh is forest, but a Knight will show you the way and in the Eighth Square we shall be Queens together and it's all feasting and fun!"

"Goodbye!" the Queen finished abruptly, and she vanished.

97

A lice ran down the hill, jumped over a
stream by some woods, and found
herself on a train going to the Third Square.

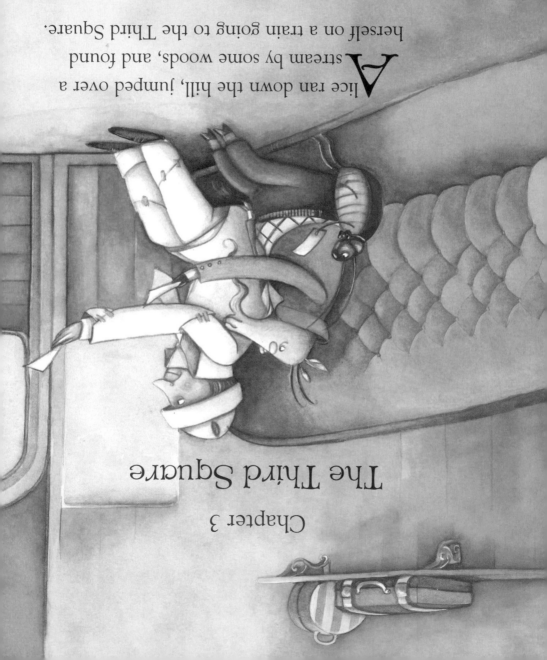

Chapter 3
The Third Square

"Ticket please!" said a Guard.
"I'm afraid I haven't got one," said Alice.

The Guard peered at her.
"You're going the wrong way,"
he announced and went off.

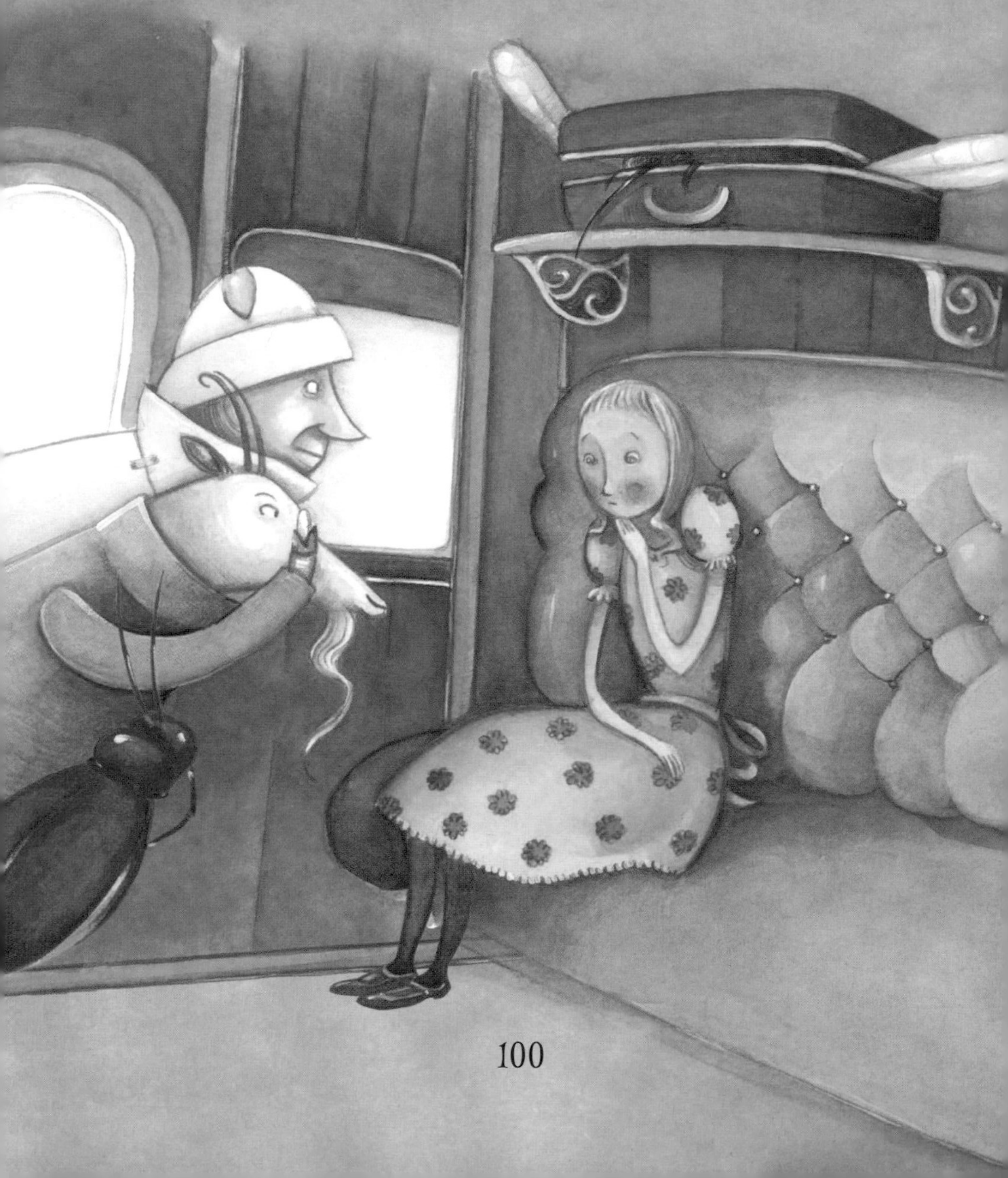

"So young a child," said the gentleman sitting opposite her (he was dressed in white paper), "ought to know which way she's going, even if she doesn't know her own name!"

A Goat, who was sitting next to him, added, "She ought to know her way to the ticket office, even if she doesn't know her alphabet."

There was a Beetle sitting next to the Goat (it was a very odd carriage-full of passengers altogether), and he went on, "She'll have to go back from here as luggage!"

"Indeed I shan't," said Alice. "I don't belong to this railway journey at all. I was by some woods just now. I wish I could get back."

"You might make a joke about that," said a tiny voice in her ear. "You know, you 'wood' if you could."

"Don't tease," said Alice, looking around to see where the voice came from.

The little voice sighed deeply, as a shrill scream from the engine made everyone jump.

The train gave a lurch
and Alice found herself
sitting under a tree,
surrounded by the
strangest insects.

The sighing voice on
the train belonged to
an enormous gnat,
who balanced on a twig
above her. It gave
another sigh and
seemed to sigh
itself away.

Alice was getting chilly sitting under the tree so she got up and walked on. She rambled across an open field and into more woods, where she came upon two signposts, both pointing the same way.

"I do believe that they live in the same house," thought Alice. "I shall go and say hello. Perhaps they can tell me the way out of these woods."

Chapter 4

Tweedledee and Tweedledum

To Tweedledum's House

To The House of TWEEDLEDEE

Alice turned a corner and came upon two little
men, each with an arm around the other's neck.
They stood so still that she quite forgot they were alive.

"If you think we're waxworks," said Tweedledum,
"you should pay."

"Contrariwise," added Tweedledee, "if you think
we're alive, you ought to speak."

"I'm sorry," said Alice. "I was wondering the best way out of these woods."

The men looked at each other and grinned.

"Do you like poetry?" asked Tweedledee, and he began to recite.

The Walrus and the Carpenter

The sun was shining on the sea
Shining with all his might:
He did his very best to make
The billows smooth and bright.
And this was odd, because it was
The middle of the night.

"If it's a very long poem," Alice said politely, "would you tell me first which road...?"
Tweedledee smiled gently and continued.

The moon was shining sulkily,
Because she thought the sun
Had got no business to be there
After the day was done.
"It's very rude of him," she said,
"To come and spoil the fun!"

...

"The time has come," the Walrus said,
"To talk of many things:
Of shoes ~ and ships ~ and sealing wax ~
Of cabbages ~ and kings ~
And why the sea is boiling hot ~
And whether pigs have wings."

...

As Tweedledee
finished, a fearsome growling
rattled the trees.

"Are there any lions or tigers around here?"
Alice asked timidly.

"It's only the Red King snoring," said Tweedledee.

"Come and look at him!" the pair said together.

"Isn't he a lovely sight?" said Tweedledum.

Alice couldn't say honestly that he was.

"What do you think he's dreaming about?"
said Tweedledee.

"Nobody can guess that," Alice said.

"Why, about you!" Tweedledee
exclaimed.

"And if he was to wake up,"
added Tweedledum, "you'd go
out – bang! – like a candle."

Alice was upset about
this, though she didn't
really believe it.

"I'd better be getting out of the woods," Alice said, "it's growing very dark. Do you think it's going to rain?"

Tweedledum looked up. "I don't think so," he began, and then he suddenly grabbed her wrist. "Do you see that?" he said, in a voice choking with passion. He pointed a trembling finger at a broken toy on the ground.

Alice looked at it. "It's only a rattle," she said. "Not a rattlesnake, you know," she added hastily, "only an old and broken rattle."

"I knew it!" cried Tweedledum, beginning to stomp around. He glared at Tweedledee. "It's spoiled."

"You needn't be so angry about an old rattle," Alice said, in a soothing voice.

"But it isn't old!" said Tweededum, furiously. "It's new! I bought it yesterday – my nice NEW rattle!" he shouted, and he started to scream.

All this time, Tweedledee was looking embarrassed. Tweedledum frowned at him.

"Of course you agree to have a battle?" Tweedledum went on, more calmly.

"I suppose so," said Tweedledee sulkily, "only she must help us dress up."

The two went off hand in hand and returned in a minute with their arms full of things – blankets, rugs, tablecloths, saucepans, buckets and an umbrella.

"I hope you're good at tying things on," Tweedledum remarked to Alice. "Every one of these things has got to go on somehow or other."

Alice had never known such a fuss made about anything in her life. "They're more like bundles of old clothes than anything else," she thought to herself.

Tweedledee insisted on having a pillow around his neck, to keep his head from being cut off.

"You know," he added gravely, "it's one of the most serious things that can possibly happen in a battle, to get one's head cut off."

Alice laughed out loud, though she managed to turn it into a cough in case she hurt his feelings.

"Do I look very pale?" asked Tweedledum.

"Well, yes, a little," replied Alice gently.

"I'm very brave generally," he said, "only today I happen to have a headache."

"And I have toothache!" said Tweedledee. "I'm far worse off than you."

"Then you'd better not fight today," said Alice.

"We must have a little fight," said Tweedledum, "but not for long. What's the time now?"

Tweedledee looked at his watch. "Half past four."

"Let's fight until six and then have dinner," said Tweedledum.

"Very well," said Tweedledee, "and she can watch us. Only you'd better not come too close," he added to Alice. "I generally hit everything I can see when I get really excited."

"And I hit everything within reach," cried Tweedledum, "whether I can see it or not!"

Alice laughed. "And all about a rattle," she said, hoping to make them feel ashamed for fighting over such a little thing.

"I shouldn't have minded so much," said Tweedledum, "if it hadn't been a new one. There's only one sword," he went on to Tweedledee, "but you can have the umbrella – it's quite as sharp. Only we must begin quickly! It's getting dark."

"And darker," said Tweedledee.

It was getting dark so suddenly that Alice thought a thunderstorm must be coming. "What a thick black cloud that is!" she said. "And how fast it comes. Why, I do believe it's got wings!"

"It's a crow!" Tweedledum cried out in alarm.

The brothers
took to their heels
and ran.

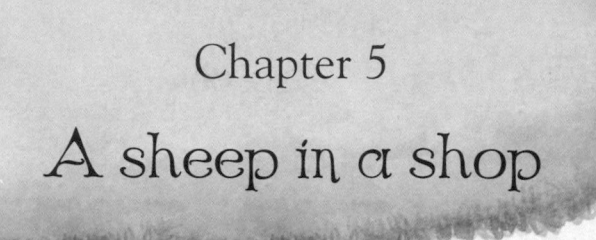

Chapter 5

A sheep in a shop

Alice took shelter under a large tree. "I wish that crow wouldn't flap its wings so," she said. "It's making quite a hurricane. Look, here's somebody's shawl being blown away."

She caught it as she spoke.

The White Queen came running wildly after the shawl and Alice went to meet her.

"I'm glad I happened to be in the way," said Alice as she helped the Queen to put on her shawl. "Dear me, what a state your hair is in," she added.

"The brush got entangled in it," the Queen said with a sigh. "And I lost the comb yesterday."

Alice carefully released the brush and did her best to get the hair into order. "That's better," she said, "but really you should have a maid."

"I'm sure I'll take you with pleasure!" the Queen said. "Tuppence a week and jam every other day."

Alice couldn't help laughing. "But I don't want you to hire me – and I don't care for jam."

"It's very good jam," said the Queen.

"Oh!" she shouted suddenly. "My finger's bleeding."

"What is the matter?" said Alice. "Have you pricked yourself?"

"Not yet," said the Queen, "but I soon shall. Oh!"

Her screams were so loud that Alice had to cover her ears.

"When I fasten my shawl again," said the Queen, "the brooch will come undone." As she spoke, the brooch flew open, the pin slipped and the Queen pricked her finger. "Well, that accounts for the bleeding," she said.

"But why don't you scream now?" asked Alice.

"I've done all the screaming already," said the Queen.

Alice frowned. "It's so hard to believe things here," she said.

"It's just practice," said the Queen. "When I was your age, I believed as many as six impossible things before breakfast. Well, I must be off."

Through the Looking-Glass

Alice stared at the Queen, who seemed to have suddenly wrapped herself up in wool. Alice blinked and looked again. Somehow, she was in a shop and a sheep was behind the counter.

"What is it you want to buy?" the Sheep said at last, looking up from her knitting.

"I don't quite know yet," Alice said. "I should like to look all around me first."

121

"You may look in front of you, and on both sides if you like," said the Sheep, "but you can't look all around you – unless you've got eyes in the back of your head."

These, as it happened, Alice had not got, so she contented herself with turning around, looking at the shelves as she came to them.

The shop seemed to be full of all manner of curious things, but the oddest part of it all was that whenever Alice looked hard at a particular shelf to make out exactly what was on it, that shelf was always quite empty, though the others around it were as full as they could be.

"Things flow about so here," she said.

"What do you want to buy?" the Sheep asked again.

"I should like an egg please," said Alice.

"You must get it for yourself," the Sheep told her and sent Alice into the darkness at the back of the shop.

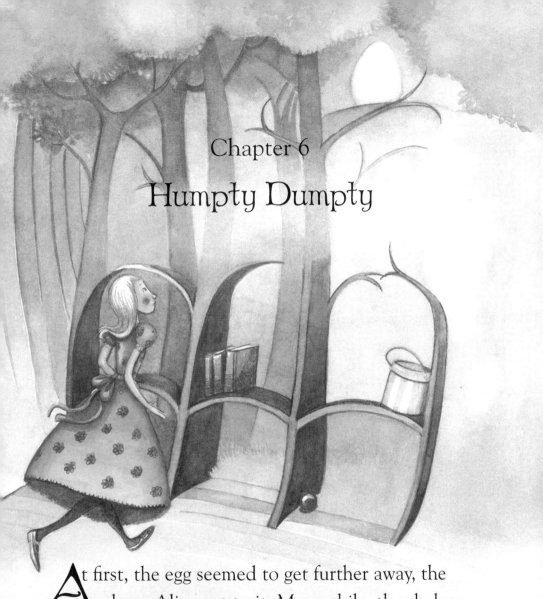

Chapter 6
Humpty Dumpty

At first, the egg seemed to get further away, the closer Alice got to it. Meanwhile, the shelves were growing branches and turning into trees.

Then the egg grew larger
and more human, and when
Alice was close enough,
she realized it was Humpty
Dumpty himself.

Humpty was sitting
with his legs crossed, on
top of a narrow, high wall.
Softly, Alice began to recite:

Humpty Dumpty sat on a wall.
Humpty Dumpty had a great fall.
All the King's horses
And all the King's men
Couldn't put Humpty together again.

125

"Don't you think you'd be safer on the ground?"
Alice asked. "That wall is so very narrow."

"Not at all," said Humpty Dumpty. "Why, if I ever
did fall off – which there's no chance of – but if I did,
the King has promised to..."

"Send all his horses and all of his men," Alice
interrupted, rather unwisely.

"Now, that's too bad!" Humpty Dumpty cried.
"You've been listening at doors – and behind trees
– and down chimneys – or you couldn't have known."

"I haven't," said Alice. "It's in a book."

"Ah," said Humpty Dumpty, "that's different."

"What a beautiful belt you've got on!" Alice
suddenly remarked.

127

"It is VERY annoying," growled Humpty Dumpty, "when a person can't tell a belt from a tie. This tie was an un-birthday present from the White King and Queen."

"What is an un-birthday present?" said Alice.

"A present you get when it isn't your birthday. There's glory for you."

"I don't know what you mean by 'glory'," Alice said.

"It means just whatever I choose," said Humpty Dumpty. "Words are tricky things, but I can manage 'em. Just listen to this poem."

Alice sighed. Everyone seemed to want to tell her poetry today. Humpty Dumpty's poem made no more sense than the others – and it didn't even have a proper ending.

> ...I took a corkscrew from the shelf.
> I went to wake them up myself.
> And when I found the door was locked,
> I pushed and pushed
> and kicked and knocked.
> And when I found the door was shut,
> I tried to turn the handle, but~

"Is that all?" said Alice.

"That's all," said Humpty Dumpty. "Goodbye."

Chapter 7

Captured!

"Really," thought Alice, as she jumped over a brook into the next square, "that egg was the most unsatisfactory person I ever met."

"Check!" called a voice.

A knight in crimson came galloping up
to Alice. "You're my prisoner!" the Knight
cried as he reached her. "You're–"

"Check!" called another voice.

Alice looked around in surprise as a White Knight galloped up.

"She's my prisoner, you know!" the Red Knight said grumpily.

"Yes, but I rescued her!" the White Knight replied.

"Well, we must fight for her, then," said the Red Knight.

The pair began hitting at each other with such fury that Alice ran back to be out of the way of the blows. If one Knight hit the other, he knocked him off his horse. If he missed, he tumbled off himself.

The battle ended when they both fell off their horses at the same time and finished up, side by side, on their heads. When they were upright, they shook hands and the Red Knight galloped off.

"It was a glorious victory!" said the White Knight.
"But I don't want to be anyone's prisoner,"
said Alice. "I want to be a Queen."

"And so you will when you've crossed the next brook," said the White Knight. "I'll see you to it and then I must go back."

"Thank you very much," said Alice.

They walked on in silence, stopping every now and then for the poor Knight, who was certainly not a good rider.

Whenever the horse stopped (which it did very often), he fell off in front, and whenever it went on again (which it generally did rather suddenly), he fell off behind. Otherwise he kept on pretty well, except that he had a habit of falling off sideways now and then.

"The great art of riding," the Knight suddenly began, waving his right arm as he spoke, "is to keep..." Here the sentence ended as suddenly as it had begun, as the Knight fell on his head. "...Is to keep your balance," he finished as Alice helped him to his feet.

And so they went on, slowly, until at last they reached the brook.

Chapter 8

Queen Alice

Alice bounded across and found herself on a soft lawn, with a crown on her head and the Red Queen and the White Queen sitting on either side.

"I invite you to Alice's dinner party this afternoon," the Red Queen said to the White Queen.

The White Queen smiled and said, "And I invite you."

"I didn't know I was to have a party," said Alice.

The White Queen gave a sigh and laid her head on Alice's shoulder. "I am so sleepy," she moaned.

"She's tired, poor thing," said the Red Queen. "Sing her a soothing lullaby."

"I don't know any," said Alice.

"I must do it myself then," said the Red Queen.

"Hush-a-by lady, in Alice's lap!
Till the feast's ready, we've time for a nap:
When the feast's over, we'll go to the ball ~
Red Queen, and White Queen, and Alice, and all!"

"And now you know the words," she added as she put her head on Alice's other shoulder. In another moment, both Queens were fast asleep and snoring gently. The snoring grew louder until...

139

...Alice found herself in a large hall filled with guests, seated between the Red and White Queens.

A waiter set a plate of meat before Alice, who looked at it nervously.

"Let me introduce you to that leg of mutton," said the Red Queen. "Alice, mutton, mutton, Alice."

"May I give you a slice?" she asked, looking from one Queen to the other.

"Certainly not!" said the Red Queen. "It's very rude to cut anyone you've been introduced to."

She called for a waiter. "Remove the mutton!" she ordered and he came to take it away.

"I don't want to be introduced to the pudding," thought Alice, "or we shall get no dinner at all."

"Do you know," Alice said, trying to make conversation, "I have had such a quantity of poetry read to me today."

"Her White Majesty knows a lovely poem that is also a riddle," said the Red Queen.

The White Queen laughed with delight and began:

First, the fish must be caught.
That is easy; a baby, I think, could have caught it.
Next, the fish must be bought.
That is easy; a penny, I think, would have bought it...

"Very nice," said the Red Queen approvingly, when it was finished. "You ought to return thanks in a speech you know," she added, frowning at Alice as she spoke.

Alice stood up. "I rise to return thanks," she began, and she really *did* rise and had to grab the table to sit back down.

"Take care of yourself!" screamed the White Queen. "Something's going to happen."

And then (as Alice afterwards described it), all sorts of things happened in a moment. The candles all grew up to the ceiling, looking like rushes with fireworks on top.

As for the bottles, they each took a pair of plates, which they put on as wings, and, with forks for legs, they went fluttering around in all directions.

"How very like birds they look," thought Alice.

At that moment she heard a hoarse laugh at her side and turned to see what was the matter with the White Queen. Instead of the Queen, there was the leg of mutton sitting in the chair.

"Here I am!" cried a voice from the soup tureen and Alice turned again, just in time to see the Queen grinning before she disappeared into the soup.

There was not a moment to be lost. Already several of the guests were lying down in the dishes and the soup ladle was walking up the table to Alice.

"I can't stand this any longer," she cried as she jumped up and seized the tablecloth with both hands. One good pull and plates, dishes, guests and candles came crashing down together in a heap on the floor.

"And as for you," she went on, turning fiercely upon the Red Queen, whom she considered as the cause of all the mischief. But the Red Queen had suddenly dwindled down to the size of a doll and was running away. "As for you," she repeated, "I'll shake you into a kitten!"

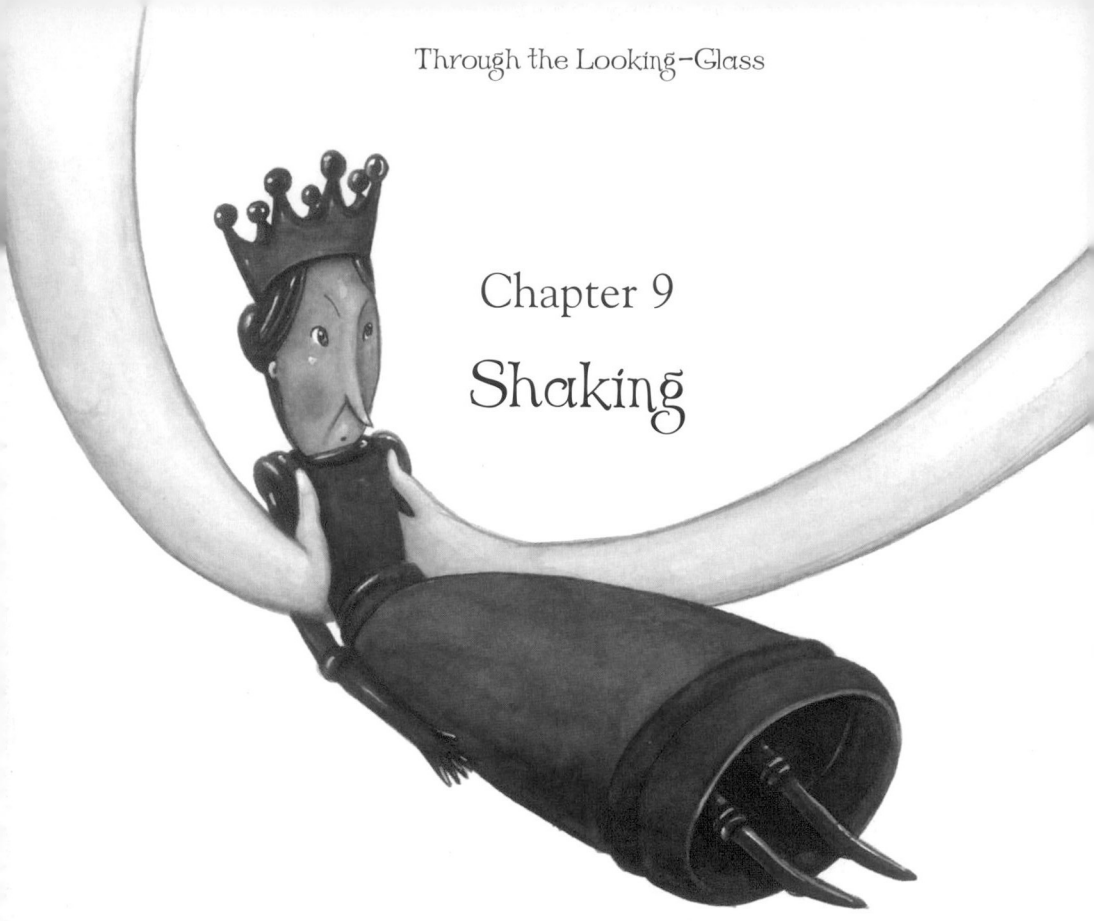

Chapter 9

Shaking

She picked her up and shook her back and forth with all her might. The Red Queen didn't say a word, but her face grew very small, and her eyes got large and green, and still as Alice went on shaking her, she kept on growing shorter... and fatter... and softer... and rounder...

Chapter 10
Waking

...and she really was a kitten, after all.

Chapter 11

Who dreamed it?

"Your majesty shouldn't purr so loud," said Alice. "You woke me out of such a nice dream. And you've been with me Kitty, all through the Looking-glass world, for I'm sure you were the Red Queen."

"The question is,"
she added, "who did dream it? It must have
been me or the Red King. He was part of my dream
but I was part of his. Was it the Red King, Kitty?"
     Which do *you* think it was?

Lewis Carroll 1832–1898

L ewis Carroll was the made-up name of Charles Lutwidge Dodgson, a lecturer in mathematics at Christ Church College, Oxford University, in England.

He was the oldest son of a clergyman and had ten brothers and sisters. From an early age, he liked making up poems, and he had a passion for literature as well as mathematics. As he grew older, he began writing articles and stories, and he developed a keen interest in photography.

He even invented new words which are now in the dictionary, including 'chortle' – a combination of 'chuckle' and 'snort'.

When he started teaching mathematics at Christ Church, he became good friends with the new Dean of the college, Henry Liddell, and his children – including his daughter Alice. They took rowing trips on the rivers in Oxford and it was on one of these trips that Lewis Carroll began to tell the children *Alice's Adventures Underground*, the story that would become *Alice's Adventures in Wonderland*. Alice's first adventures were published in 1865. The sequel, set in the looking-glass world, was published six years later.

The Poems in the Alice Stories

"Do you know I have had such a quantity of poetry said to me today," Alice says to the Red Queen in *Through the Looking-Glass*. Both *Alice's Adventures in Wonderland* and *Through the Looking-Glass* are full of Lewis Carroll's nonsense poems. Some are his version of famous poems of the day – such as *Twinkle, Twinkle Little Bat* which was based upon *Twinkle, Twinkle Little Star*. Others are completely made-up – even down to the made-up words he used in them.

Many were too long to include in the adaptations of the stories, so a selection of his best-loved poems are printed here in full. After the last poem, *Jabberwocky*, you will find a glossary to all the nonsense words in the first verse.

How Doth the Little Crocodile

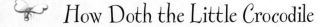

How doth the little crocodile
Improve his shining tail,
And pour the waters of the Nile
On every golden scale!

How cheerfully he seems to grin,
How neatly spreads his claws,
And welcomes little fishes in,
With gently smiling jaws!

This was based on a poem called
How Doth the Little Busy Bee.

153

Humpty Dumpty's Song

In winter, when the fields are white,
I sing this song for your delight:
In spring, when woods are getting green,
I'll try and tell you what I mean:
In summer, when the days are long,
Perhaps you'll understand the song:
In autumn, when the leaves are brown,
Take pen and ink, and write it down.
I sent a message to the fish:
I told them "This is what I wish."
The little fishes of the sea,
They sent an answer back to me.
The little fishes' answer was
"We cannot do it, Sir, because~"
I sent to them again to say
"It will be better to obey."
The fishes answered, with a grin,
"Why, what a temper you are in!"
I told them once, I told them twice:

They would not listen to advice.
I took a kettle large and new,
Fit for the deed I had to do.
My heart went hop, my heart went thump:
I filled the kettle at the pump.
Then someone came to me and said,
"The little fishes are in bed."
I said to him, I said it plain,
"Then you must wake them up again."
I said it very loud and clear:
I went and shouted in his ear.
But he was very stiff and proud:
He said, "You needn't shout so loud!"
And he was very proud and stiff:
He said, "I'd go and wake them, if~"
I took a corkscrew from the shelf.
I went to wake them up myself.
And when I found the door was locked,
I pulled and pushed and kicked and knocked.
And when I found the door was shut,
I tried to turn the handle, but~

(The poem ends here.)

The Walrus and the Carpenter

The sun was shining on the sea,
Shining with all his might:
He did his very best to make
The billows smooth and bright.
And this was odd, because it was
The middle of the night.

The moon was shining sulkily
Because she thought the sun
Had got no business to be there
After the day was done.
"It's very rude of him," she said,
"To come and spoil the fun!"

The sea was wet as wet could be,
The sands were dry as dry.
You could not see a cloud, because
No cloud was in the sky:
No birds were flying overhead ~
There were no birds to fly.

The Walrus and the Carpenter
Were walking close at hand;
They wept like anything to see
Such quantities of sand:
"If this were only cleared away,"
They said, "it would be grand!"

"If seven maids with seven mops
Swept it for half a year,
Do you suppose," the Walrus said,
"That they could get it clear?"
"I doubt it," said the Carpenter,
And shed a bitter tear.

"O Oysters, come and walk with us!"
The Walrus did beseech.
"A pleasant walk, a pleasant talk,
Along the briny beach:
We cannot do with more than four,
To give a hand to each."

The eldest Oyster looked at him
But never a word he said.
The eldest Oyster winked his eye,
And shook his heavy head,
Meaning to say he did not choose
To leave the oyster-bed.

But four young oysters hurried up,
All eager for the treat:
Their coats were brushed, their faces washed,
Their shoes were clean and neat.
And this was odd, because, you know,
They hadn't any feet.

Four other Oysters followed them,
And yet another four;
And thick and fast they came at last,
And more, and more, and more ~
All hopping through the frothy waves,
And scrambling to the shore.

The Walrus and the Carpenter
Walked on a mile or so,
And then they rested on a rock
Conveniently low:
And all the little Oysters stood
And waited in a row.

"The time has come," the Walrus said,
"To talk of many things:
Of shoes ~ and ships ~ and sealing-wax ~
Of cabbages ~ and kings ~
And why the sea is boiling hot ~
And whether pigs have wings."

"But wait a bit," the Oysters cried,
    "Before we have our chat;
For some of us are out of breath,
    And all of us are fat!"
"No hurry!" said the Carpenter.
They thanked him much for that.

"A loaf of bread," the Walrus said,
    "Is what we chiefly need:
Pepper and vinegar besides
    Are very good indeed.
Now if you're ready Oysters dear,
    We can begin to feed."

"But not on us!" the Oysters cried,
    Turning a little blue,
"After such kindness, that would be
    A dismal thing to do!"
"The night is fine," the Walrus said
    "Do you admire the view?"

"It was so kind of you to come!
And you are very nice!"
The Carpenter said nothing but,
"Cut us another slice:
I wish you were not quite so deaf ~
I've had to ask you twice!"

"It seems a shame," the Walrus said,
"To play them such a trick,
After we've brought them out so far,
And made them trot so quick!"
The Carpenter said nothing but,
"The butter's spread too thick!"

"I weep for you," the Walrus said.
"I deeply sympathize."
With sobs and tears he sorted out
Those of the largest size,
Holding his pocket handkerchief
Before his streaming eyes.

"O Oysters," said the Carpenter,
"You've had a pleasant run!
Shall we be trotting home again?"
But answer came there none ~
And this was scarcely odd, because
They'd eaten every one.

The White Queen's Poem

First, the fish must be caught.
That is easy: a baby, I think, could have caught it.
Next, the fish must be bought.
That is easy: a penny, I think, would have bought it.

Now cook me the fish!
That is easy and will not take more than a minute.
Let it lie in a dish!
That is easy because it already is in it.

Bring it here! Let me sup!
It is easy to set such a dish on the table.
Take the dish-cover up!
Ah, that is so hard that I fear I'm unable!

For it holds it like glue ~
Holds the lid to the dish, while it lies in the middle:
Which is easiest to do,
Un-dish-cover the fish, or dishcover the riddle?

The Letter in the Trial

(This is read out by the White Rabbit
at the Knave of Hearts' trial.)

They told me you had been to her,
And mentioned me to him:
She gave me a good character,
But said I could not swim.

He sent them word I had not gone
(We know it to be true):
If she should push the matter on,
What would become of you?

I gave her one, they gave him two,
You gave us three or more;
They all returned from him to you,
Though they were mine before.

If I or she should chance to be
Involved in this affair,
He trusts to you to set them free,
Exactly as we were.

My notion was that you had been
(Before she had this fit)
An obstacle that came between
Him, and ourselves, and it.

Don't let him know she liked them best,
For this must ever be
A secret, kept from all the rest,
Between yourself and me.

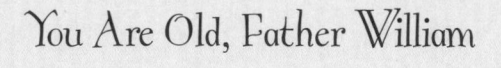

You Are Old, Father William

"You are old, father William," the young man said,
"And your hair has become very white;
And yet you incessantly stand on your head ~
Do you think, at your age, it is right?"

"In my youth," father William replied to his son,
"I feared it might injure the brain;
But now that I'm perfectly sure I have none,
Why, I do it again and again."

"You are old," said the youth, "as I mentioned before,
And have grown most uncommonly fat;
Yet you turned a back-somersault in at the door.
Pray what is the reason for that?"

"In my youth," said the sage, as he shook his grey locks,
"I kept all my limbs very supple
By the use of this ointment ~ one shilling the box.
Allow me to sell you a couple?"

166

"You are old," said the youth, "and your jaws are too weak
For anything tougher than suet;
Yet you finished the goose, with the bones and the beak
Pray, how did you manage to do it?"

"In my youth," said his father, "I took to the law,
And argued each case with my wife;
And the muscular strength, which it gave to my jaw,
Has lasted the rest of my life."

"You are old," said the youth, "one would hardly suppose
That your eye was as steady as ever;
Yet you balanced an eel on the end of your nose.
What made you so awfully clever?"

"I have answered three questions, and that is enough,"
Said his father. "Don't give yourself airs!
Do you think I can listen all day to such stuff?
Be off, or I'll kick you down stairs!"

The White Knight's Song

I'll tell thee everything I can:
There's little to relate.
I saw an aged, aged man,
A-sitting on a gate.
"Who are you, aged man?" I said,
"And how is it you live?"
And his answer trickled through my head,
Like water through a sieve.

He said, "I look for butterflies
That sleep among the wheat:
I make them into mutton-pies,
And sell them in the street.
I sell them unto men," he said,
"Who sail on stormy seas;
And that's the way I get my bread ~
A trifle, if you please."

But I was thinking of a plan
To dye one's whiskers green,
And always use so large a fan
That they could not be seen.
So, having no reply to give
To what the old man said,
I cried, "Come, tell me how you live!"
And thumped him on the head.

His accents mild took up the tale:
He said, "I go my ways,
And when I find a mountain-rill,
I set it in a blaze;
And thence they make a stuff they call
Rowland's Macassar Oil ~
Yet twopence-halfpenny is all
They give me for my toil."

But I was thinking of a way
To feed oneself on batter,
And so go on from day to day
Getting a little fatter.
I shook him well from side to side,
Until his face was blue:
"Come, tell me how you live," I cried,
"And what it is you do!"

He said, "I hunt for haddocks' eyes
Among the heather bright,
And work them into waistcoat buttons
In the silent night.
And these I do not sell for gold
Or coin of silvery shine,
But for a copper halfpenny,
And that will purchase nine.

"I sometimes dig for buttered rolls,
Or set limed twigs for crabs:
I sometimes search the grassy knolls
For wheels of Hansom-cabs.
And that's the way," (he gave a wink),
"By which I get my wealth ~
And very gladly will I drink
Your Honour's noble health."

I heard him then, for I had just
Completed my design
To keep the Menai bridge from rust
By boiling it in wine.
I thanked him much for telling me
The way he got his wealth,
But chiefly for his wish that he
Might drink my noble health.

And now, if e'er by chance I put
My fingers into glue,
Or madly squeeze a right-hand foot
Into a left-hand shoe,
Or if I drop upon my toe
A very heavy weight,
I weep, for it reminds me so
Of that old man I used to know ~

Whose look was mild, whose speech was slow,
Whose hair was whiter than the snow,
Whose face was very like a crow,
With eyes, like cinders, all aglow,
Who seemed distracted with his woe,
Who rocked his body to and fro,
And muttered mumblingly and low,
As if his mouth were full of dough,
Who snorted like a buffalo ~
That summer evening long ago,
A-sitting on a gate.

Jabberwocky

'Twas brillig, and the slithy toves
Did gyre and gimble in the wabe;
All mimsy were the borogoves,
And the mome raths outgrabe.

"Beware the Jabberwock, my son!
The jaws that bite, the claws that catch!
Beware the Jubjub bird, and shun
The frumious Bandersnatch!"

He took his vorpal sword in hand:
Long time the manxome foe he sought ~
So rested he by the Tumtum tree,
And stood awhile in thought.

And as in uffish thought he stood,
The Jabberwock, with eyes of flame,
Came whiffling through the tulgey wood,
And burbled as it came!

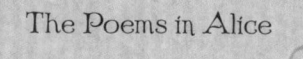

One, two! One, two! And through and through
The vorpal blade went snicker-snack!
He left it dead, and with its head
He went galumphing back.

"And hast thou slain the Jabberwock?
Come to my arms, my beamish boy!
O frabjous day! Callooh! Callay!"
He chortled in his joy.

'Twas brillig, and the slithy toves
Did gyre and gimble in the wabe;
All mimsy were the borogoves,
And the mome raths outgrabe.

Glossary for the first verse of Jabberwocky

In the full version of *Through the Looking-Glass*,
when Alice is talking to Humpty Dumpty, he tells her
the meaning of some of the words in *Jabberwocky*.

Brillig: four o'clock in the afternoon – the time when you begin broiling (or grilling) things for dinner.
Slithy: lithe and slimy. ('Lithe' is the same as 'active'.)
Toves: creatures that are a cross between badgers, lizards and corkscrews. They make their nests under sundials and live on cheese.
To gyre: to go round and round like a gyroscope.
To gimble: to make holes like a gimblet.
Wabe: the grass around a sundial, so-called because it goes a long way before it and a long way behind it. (And a long way beyond it on each side.)
Mimsy: flimsy and miserable.
Borogove: a thin, shabby bird with its feathers sticking out all around it – rather like a live mop.
Mome rath: a *rath* is a sort of green pig and Humpty Dumpty thinks *mome* is short for 'from home' – in other words, they'd lost their way.
To outgrabe: this is to make a sound between a bellow and a whistle, with a kind of sneeze in the middle.

Usborne Quicklinks

For links to websites where you can find out about the real Alice, look inside the original manuscript of *Alice's Adventures Underground* and print out some of Lewis Carroll's poems, go to the Usborne Quicklinks Website at **www.usborne-quicklinks.com** and type in the keywords "illustrated alice".

The recommended websites are regularly reviewed and updated but, please note, Usborne Publishing is not responsible for the content of any website other than its own. We recommend that children are supervised while using the internet.

First published in 2009 by Usborne Publishing Ltd,
83-85 Saffron Hill, London EC1N 8RT, England.
www.usborne.com Copyright © 2009 Usborne Publishing Ltd.
The name Usborne and the devices ♈☝ are Trade Marks of Usborne Publishing Ltd.
First published in America in 2009. UE. Printed in China.